GHOST STORIES: 25 SUPERNATURAL TALES BY REAL PEOPLE BASED ON TRUE EVENTS IN AND AROUND THE FAR EAST

First edition. April 7, 2022.

ISBN: 979-8201648480

Written by Granger T Barr.

Also by Granger T Barr

Table of Contents

GHOST STORIES

25 Supernatural Tales

By Real People Based On

True Events In And Around

The Far East

Granger T Barr

Disclaimer Notice

Please note that the information contained in this book is for entertainment purposes only. All effort has been made to ensure the information is up-to-date, reliable, and complete. However, no warranties of any kind are declared or implied. The content of this book has been derived from various sources.

By reading this book, the reader agrees that under no circumstances is the author responsible for any losses, direct or indirect, incurred from the use of this book. Including but not limited to errors, omissions, or inaccuracies.

While every precaution has been taken in preparing this book, the author and publisher assume no responsibility for any errors or omissions. This includes any damages resulting from using the information contained in this book.

All personal accounts from individuals have been given permission; however, their identity remains anonymous.

Other Books by This Author

You may be interested in other books within the Ghostly Encounters Series:

True Ghost Stories and Hauntings: Real-Life Personal Short Ghost Stories In And Around Britain

13 short ghost stories.

Real Ghost Stories and Hauntings: True-Life Short Ghost Stories (*Ghostly Paranormal Encounters*)

19 short ghost stories.

True Ghost Stories & Hauntings Chilling Tales For Adults: Real Life Paranormal Ghostly Supernatural Encounters Collection From Around The World.

GET A FREE GHOST E-BOOK BY SUBSCRIBING TO OUR MAILING LIST[1]:

Get more freebies, goodies and instant new book release announcements!

https://digitaldome.sendibble.com/True-Ghost-Stories-Perma-Free-Ghost-E-book

---

1. *https://digitaldome.sendibble.com/True-Ghost-Stories-Perma-Free-Ghost-E-book*

Introduction

———

Many people have met and interviewed me on my travels and stories from around the world. However, I've discovered that their ghost stories varied depending on my encountered cultures.

In my previous six volumes, I chronicled authentic, real-life human stories primarily from the Western world, including the United Kingdom, America, and others.

On the other hand, this book comprises 25 stories of supernatural events from diverse locales in and around the Far East. I hope you enjoy reading these.

The Lost Boy

———

I had an unsettling encounter with the spirit of a small child, maybe between the ages of two and four, who used to wander around the neighbourhood where we live.

During the day, he would simply walk into a room, never moving or making a sound, yet he always seemed sad.

My two-year-old could also see him since he tried to connect with him and gave him toys.

We could see him standing at the window, peeping and keeping an eye on us one day while we were playing in the garden, and when we went home, he would be waiting at the front window.

I used to feel terrible for him because he appeared to want to be a part of the group or family and possibly needed cuddling.

However, it became increasingly terrible as the night progressed. Finally, even though that was the only time he talked, we never saw or heard from him again.

Instead, he'd run up and down the stairs, sobbing furiously.

One day, my two-year-old asked me in the kitchen, "Where is Stephen's mummy?" I looked around, but there was no one. When I asked who Stephen was, he said the youngster's name was Stephen and pointed to the corridor. Then he remarked that Stephen had been depressed since he had lost his mother.

We were able to get the services of a local priest after around six months.

According to him, a young mother and her child were killed in their home 40 years ago in a fire that broke out while they were sleeping, and he could sense the boy's soul couldn't rest because he had been torn from his beloved mother.

The priest sprayed holy water all over the boy and prayed for him. He was pleading with God to reunite them. Following that, I felt a profound sense of calmness and quiet. The priest assured me that the child had returned to his mother and was now at peace.

It was the most emotional thing I'd ever seen, and my mother and I just sat there sobbing the entire time I gave her the story.

Unfortunately, we never saw or heard anything else about the little man.

When I was researching the location, former residents, and so on, I looked him up on the internet and discovered his name was Stephen.

Ghost Festival Month

This occurrence occurred around the same year and month as the Ghost Festival.

I was in primary 5 or 6, so I was still quite little at the time. Every year during the 7th month, the "thing" would be celebrated with an opera performance just below our apartment block, and tentages would be set up for praying purposes just below our apartment block.

But, of course, we were kids back then, and my neighbours and I used to enjoy walking down to the bottom of the block to play catching or soccer.

On this particular day, everyone in the group agreed to go down and play block catching.

The rules were determined before the games; we were only allowed to ascend to the fifth level and no higher.

We were all on the same page. My acquaintance was chosen to act as the game's catcher. It's time to get started!

But instead of running about, I went to the back alley of the block, where it was dark, and I was convinced they wouldn't be able to find me.

I remained there after a while, and no one came to look for me, which was weird.

I decided to go home, and when I got there, I saw all of my friend's gathering, waiting for me because they couldn't find me. So I decided to go home.

I had been tired all day and had decided to retire to bed.

For a while, everything seemed to be going OK until I awoke mid-sleep.

I was somewhat aback to discover myself nicely tucked in and lying down in a perfectly upright position.

I noticed my father seated at the computer table when I raised my head, but the computer was switched off. It was getting a little weird, so I sat down and then lifted my head to take another look around the room.

Instead of my father, I saw a woman with long black hair and a white robe. Because my mother's hair was not so long and brownish, I quickly recognised them as hers.

Despite my terror, I remained immobile in my bed, covering my eyes with my blanket until I fell asleep. I was petrified.

When I awoke the following day, I noticed my father and asked him, "Hey dad, this morning you came back early, ah?" "Did you happen to sit at my computer table earlier?" I inquired.

He responded by saying he had just gotten home from work. He notified my mother, and they decided to take me to a nearby temple.

The man at the table, seated with two others, informed me that I had insulted a spirit and asked that I apologise.

He also said that I had accidentally stepped on something, causing the spirit to become upset with me because I was completely unaware of what had occurred.

I drank it while holding a talisman that had been burned in it.

And I never had another episode like that in my room after that.

Remember that you should never be flippant during a specific month because you never know who you might have offended. It is always preferable to be safe rather than sorry.

The Woman Sitting On The Bed

———

A few months ago, I awoke to see a young blonde-haired girl standing to my right, smiling and looking at me.

When the alarm went off, I turned around to see her standing there. It was a little dark, but there was enough light to see her standing there, and I figured I was still asleep, possibly half-dreaming.

Instead, he just lay there staring at her in awe.

After unsuccessfully attempting to get out of bed, I slid and fell back into bed.

I remember rubbing my eyes, hoping that she would disappear; she eventually did, but slowly; she gradually faded away.

My husband asked what was wrong with me, but I couldn't speak because I was too scared, and my heart was beating, so I ultimately told him.

My spouse had to turn on the bathroom and toilet lights because I was so scared up, and they have remained on ever since while I sleep.

I sincerely hope I never see her again since I was afraid of her.

She sat there, hands on her knees, facing the opposite direction.

When he asked what she was doing, I told him she was getting up and heading toward the stairway.

At first, he thought it was his ex-girlfriend. She, however, committed suicide several years before he met and married me.

Although I was unconcerned before seeing the girl, it was the way she walked away slowly with a grin that worried me. So strange.

Slamming Doors

———

L ast year, renovations were underway at a branch of a family-friendly restaurant popular with Naval Servicemen and soldiers. However, a portion of it remained open to the general public.

I needed to use the restroom quickly one night, around 10 pm.

Our car pulled into the parking lot, and my companion sat in it until we got inside.

I entered the parking through the front counter (a pay machine, a top-up machine, and a security guard sitting behind his desk) and then rode the elevator up to the 3rd or 4th floor, where the Chinese restaurant was located.

If you remember the layout, turn right as you exit the lift, and you'll be in the Chinese restaurant. The public restroom is only a short walk away.

The air was calm, and the surrounding region was black when I stepped out of the lift that night. It was an odd sensation.

Nobody was on that floor, and the restaurant hadn't even opened yet. So it was very tranquil, and there was no breeze at all.

When I entered the public restroom, I was shocked to see no one else there.

I went about my business, cleaned my hands, and departed the restroom, returning to the lift. I was finished.

I heard a loud slamming sound behind me after reaching the top of the stairs and pressing the down button, which I immediately recognised a toilet cubicle door closing behind me.

I paused for a fraction of a second, as nothing had happened, and then pressed the "down" button while waiting for the lift to take me to the parking garage.

The smashing sound could be heard again. It sounded like someone was pounding the cubicle door shut in the toilet.

When the elevator arrived, I entered silently and pressed the basement button – as the lift door closed, I could still hear cubicle doors slamming in the background.

When I arrived at the carpark, I asked the security man if anyone was on the floor.

He looked at me and told me that the building was being refurbished and that there was no one on that floor.

I enquired whether he was certain. He then looked at me and asked whether I was all right. As a result, I cautioned him that the floor might not be as clean as it should be. He then gave me a funny expression.

My companion gazed at me with astonishment while walking back to the car, commenting that I appeared incredibly pale and drenched in sweat.

Haunted Statues

———

There are rumours that Haw Par Villa is haunted, which you dismiss out of hand because how can a collection of garishly painted statues ever be terrifying? Then there are the mythical Ten Courts of Hell, but each diorama is made to look more like something from a cartoon than anything from a horror film.

I'm not entirely wrong - none of the sculptures in the exhibition appears to be haunted.

However, not all statues are on display, and there is a strong reason.

The possessed statues were swiftly removed from the premises by the security personnel.

However, tradition has it that walking near the sculptures leads you to hear things - spirits screaming for vengeance, souls crying for a better life, and if you're lucky, the sculptures may even start moving.

And who knows, if you come too close, they might just manage to possess you.

This is what I discovered when I visited this location. I can hear faint crying.

It was terrifying, but when I questioned the security guy about what that noise may have been, he described what it could have been. He claimed that no guards would work near there at night.

Instead, the location contains C.C.T. cameras, which have captured white mist circling some of the painted sculptures and stone statues on numerous occasions.

The Hostel Bunk Bed

———

I visited Bangkok for the first time in 2001. Before my trip, I researched online to find a cheap hostel room in Bangkok, which I booked through Expedia.

I chose to stay at this upscale hostel in private house development.

The hostel was four floors tall. I was put in a room with four other ladies on the top floor.

When I arrived at the hostel, it was long past midnight, and I checked in.

I unlocked the bedroom door quietly to not wake up the two fast asleep travellers in their beds.

Because the lower bunks of the double-decker beds were already occupied, I chose the upper bunk.

When I awoke the following day, I was utterly alone. The two female tourists had already checked out the hostel.

After a late-night the first night, I returned to the hostel the following night. I opened the door to my bedroom and discovered that I had the entire place to myself for the night.

That was not a problem for me because I was used to sleeping alone in my room.

As soon as I completed cleaning, I moved my items from the top bunk of the same bed to the bottom bunk of another bed.

I had already fallen asleep by this time, and the air conditioner had begun to cool the room.

However, before falling asleep, I had a one-of-a-kind experience that I wanted to relate to.

A notion went into my mind, questioning what I would do if the bed began to shake.

The double-decker bed began to tremble violently for a few seconds as I mentioned it!

I did only pretend nothing had happened and hid under the duvet as if nothing had happened.

I reasoned that ignoring the problem would eventually cause 'it' to give up and leave me alone.

Seconds later, a strange cool air swept just under my blanket from an unknown source behind my left shoulder, and I leapt out of bed to find out what it was.

There couldn't be any wind from the air conditioning unit because it was located over the double-decker bed.

I awoke the next day feeling fine and ready to go. Unfortunately, I could not express what occurred last night despite my best attempts.

So I prepared to visit Bangkok that day and returned late that night.

I had second thoughts about sleeping alone in that room by the third day. As much as I wanted to leave and find another hostel, I couldn't.

When I arrived for the first night, I had already paid in full for a four-night stay.

Because I was unaware of my right to request a room change at the time of the occurrence, I did not exercise it.

So I forced myself to spend another two nights in that spooky chamber, which was well worth it.

After cleaning up, I lingered outside the room where I sat on a couch and watched television.

I reasoned that staying up late would allow me to increase my time in that room.

A tired body and mind, on the other hand, were in desperate need of rest. So I had no choice but to retire to my bed.

I spotted a tall, slim translucent white apparition standing directly in front of me beside the bed's head as I stood by the double-decker bed before falling in during my last few moments.

I couldn't make out its face; all I saw was its lanky torso, which lacked arms and hands. It appeared to be dressed in a white robe.

Then it vanished in an instant as if it had never existed.

Surprisingly, I did not have any interruptions that night or the next.

As time went on, I never returned to that hostel and never understood how a bed could tremble on its own without any apparent cause.

The Elderly Lady

It was raining and dark outside when I heard several loud pounding on the door.

"Selling keropok...selling keropok," a Malay voice says on the other side of the door.

When I open the door, an elderly makcik greets me with a kind smile. I consider it as nothing more than a shill.

"Thank you, but I do not need keropok." Then I say something as I fight to close the door.

"Selling keropok... selling keropok," she continues, her cheeks bright. I quickly turn aside, but the hairs on my neck stand up. When I turn back, the smiling makcik has vanished.

Instead, there sits a Pontianak, who is thought to be the makcik keropok's curse.

She's an elderly woman who wanders around H.D.B. estates peddling keropok and is said to be a witch.

If you do not buy keropok from her soon, your house will be cursed, or she may release a Pontianak into your home, depending on your reaction.

I noticed an elderly woman dressed in white with black hair clutching two plastic bags one night.

Even though sightings of makcik keropok have decreased over the years, I believe the story has survived as Singapore's longest-lasting urban legend.

If you believe she exists, you should keep your door locked if she comes knocking.

The Man

———

I'm a medium and come from a spiritualist family. However, they can be unrealistic because I've only had a few encounters, but I've captured orbs on film and voices on tape.

When I was younger, I had a cat who died, and I once saw him come into my mother's bedroom as bold as brass.

Because it was a hot summer and the door was left open, I initially imagined it was a cat slipping in through the rear door, but as I came into the room.

There was no such thing. My father died of lung cancer at 56, and I had a weird gut sensation that something was not proper for days.

My father had complained about a man standing behind him at this moment.

He was bedridden and slept in our living room while my younger brother and sister were downstairs playing.

He was no longer alive when we arrived home. He died as a result of lung cancer.

Singapore Soul Catcher

———

We lived on landed property when I was a kid, and one night between 3 and 4 am, I overheard my father let out the most extended, bloodcurdling scream I'd ever heard in my life – like, a full-on horror movie scream.

I then heard footsteps shuffle up the stairwell at a snail's rate.

When I awoke, no one else was awake, and because my room was directly in front of the stairs, I realised, to my increasing horror, that someone was in the house and was on its way straight to my bedroom.

I did what any other adolescent would do: I hid beneath my blankets when terrified. However, my idiotic self at the time disliked sleeping with the doors closed, so I chose to put a full-length mirror immediately in front of my bed for whatever reason.

Of course, it had come to a complete standstill outside my door, and I knew that if I looked out from under my blankets, I'd either see it in person or the mirror.

Whatever transpired after that is a fog to me; however, the creature didn't seem to do anything else. So I assume I merely laid under the cover, terrified, until the time I usually wake up.

It was natural for me to wonder why my father was yelling in the middle of the night.

" I imagined I saw myself on a bed, and there was a black shadow or whatever hanging over me, and it was attempting to pull my friggin soul from my body," he explained.

He was screaming in pain and terror, and the only reason he was still alive was because of another white light.

He characterised it as feeling like my late grandmother was close, seeking to shield him from whatever devil this creature was targeting.

Unfortunately, we have no idea what the thing was, and it has not happened since.

This is the scariest experience I've ever had, and as a result, I now keep my doors closed at all times.

Night Of Terror

———

I t happened when I was eight, and it happened at this Malaysian resort. Everything was going swimmingly as a group of two families... until the second night.

Because we were the youngest siblings in both houses, my friend and I slept in the room across the hall from the kitchen. It was the bungalow's single room on the first floor, and it was modest.

On the second night, my friend and I got into an argument about a game we were playing shortly before bed, and she ended up sleeping with her parents the next night.

I was obstinate and refused to accept my parents' offer to sleep with them, despite feeling completely comfortable doing so. It was the worst decision I'd ever made.

It was around 1 am when the temperature began to plummet dramatically. When I heard knocks on the windows, I was in the middle of adjusting the air conditioner.

It knocked every window in its path and travelled from one to the next. I froze, not knowing whether my mind or ears were playing tricks on me. The story, however, did not end there.

I awoke at 3 am to the loud movement of furniture in the living room. When I stepped outside my room, I discovered that the dining chairs were scattered throughout the dining area! So, after placing the chairs back where they belonged, I proceeded into the living room.

The television went on by itself as soon as I sat down in front of it, displaying nothing but black and white static. Then, just as I was about to reach for the remote, it chose to turn itself off.

My tears streamed down my cheeks, but I couldn't force myself to speak. But then, I was startled by a noise coming from the kitchen on my way to my room.

I observed a pile of what appeared to be black and white static in the kitchen, but it turned out to be a swarm of ants on a white towel, which I soon removed. THE BACK DOOR ABRUPTLY SWUNG OPEN when I let out a small yell.

Unfortunately, there was a lot of wind, and when I tried to close the door, it wouldn't move - it felt like it was being dragged from outside. Then it gave way, and I was able to close it swiftly.

"OK, I'm going up to my parents' room to sleep," I thought. I checked the time and noticed that it was 5.30 am. I decided to put up with it because we had to wake up at 6.30 am for breakfast, and it was just another hour. Another blunder has been made.

I went upstairs to the living room, which had a second set of sofas, a television, and a tiny coffee table, among other things.

On the second story, there was also a little balcony. I fell asleep on the couch after a few minutes of silence.

There were additional knocks on the door after that!

Even though there were just three full-length glass panes this time, there were three to five knocks on each pane back and forth.

Amid my terror, the television turned on again, displaying the same black and white static before turning off and repeating the sequence. I checked my wristwatch and saw that it was already 6 am.

I calmed myself down and went into my parents' room, pretending to make a phone call to rouse them awake.

This happened in 2001 at a resort with a history of awful deaths, and I didn't find out about it until months later when I read a few articles about the resort in the newspaper.

The Local Phantom

———

My grandmother was originally from Ireland. When we were younger, she told my cousins and me terrible stories about a banshee, otherwise known as a water demon in Asia.

In one of her earlier stories, she described how she and her sister Pat went on an errand for their mother when they were 13 years old. They had to travel through a wooded area to get to their objective.

Children enjoyed fishing and playing in a tiny creek that flowed through the woods. The two of them were approaching the stream from a distance when Pat asked Gran, *'What's that?'*

They both came to a complete stop and peered. A woman stood near the stream, her back to them, and she said nothing.

Her hair was long and dark, and she was dressed in a light-coloured outfit. Her feet were completely naked but turned backwards.

All of the girls kept their voices down to hear the woman's calm, gentle sobbing.

Then, finally, my grandmother and her sister turned and bolted in the opposite direction as quickly as possible without pausing to think about what they were about to do.

The next day, they went home and told their father about their trip; their mother was displeased that they had returned without finishing their task.

Their father speculated that it was most likely the local phantom. There was nothing more their mother could do but roll her eyes and say something under her breath.

The body of a young girl was discovered the following day by a passing motorist.

She was found lying face down in the stream, in the same spot where the weeping woman had lain down earlier.

According to legend, the banshee arrives right before a disaster or death occurs.

Mental Patients

———

The first thing you notice is the almost pungent aroma of frangipani in the air, which lingers for quite some time. After that, you start to hear voices.

As they walk around the halls, murmuring and whispering their stories to everyone who will listen, they become a nuisance.

Tales of the demons in their brains, tales of what life was like in the past when a hospital could no longer accommodate them.

They're completely harmless. As you stand there, surrounded by the sounds of long-dead mental patients; who have been imprisoned in the hospital for all time, you are overcome with claustrophobia.

Who they are, and what do they do? Well, the capacity of this particular hospital was reached in 1985, prompting the construction of a second facility hospital to house psychiatric patients.

The spirits of the mental patients are still stuck in the hospital, just as they were during their physical lives.

They have no way to leave, just like their physical bodies.

They have no bodily form because they are spirits rather than ghosts.

So, you may not be able to see them, but you will be able to tell when one is nearby.

The Haunted Railway

———

One of my secondary school friends lived near Tanglin Halt, close to the Catholic Church and the Hindu temple.

A railway track ran from Tanjong Pagar Railway Station to Bukit Merah, Tanglin Halt, Buona Vista tunnel, Bukit Timah, Woodlands Checkpoint, and Johor Bahru in Malaysia. The track was decommissioned in 2009.

Trains arriving from Malaysia will travel in the same direction as those departing from Singapore.

My friend's building and kitchen window are just across the street from the train track. He claims that the trains will pass by at all day hours, making it extremely noisy.

A trail leads across the railroad lines to the woodland region across his block. According to him, there are some colonial homes there as well, but no one or a small number of people will reside there.

After dusk, that part of town will be deafeningly quiet.

One morning, after going to the bathroom, he noticed an elderly gentleman walking down the railroad lines and glanced out the window, intrigued.

On its route to Tanjong Pagar, an incoming train passed the old man, who was no longer there after the train had passed. He returned to his bed as soon as he realised he was feeling strange. When we met up at school the next day, he told me about the incident.

When returning from tuition at night, his neighbour's son saw a lady in white sitting on one of the trees opposite the track, with a grin on her face from the corner of his eye.

While pretending that he didn't see anything, he instantly went upstairs.

During the 9th month, my friend's mother awoke one morning to close the windows in her bedroom because it was starting to drizzle outside, and the room overlooked a railway track. She also noticed an elderly woman and a young child walking away from her, their backs to her, directly into the railway tracks.

According to local legend, that railway route leads to a supposedly haunted tunnel beneath Buona Vista.

Old Farmhouse

———

I grew up on a rural farm, where I now live. It was an old farmhouse that had been constructed in the 1850s. Strange things happened regularly.

When you place an object on the ground, it will disappear, only to reappear later in the exact location.

Because we lived on a farm, we had many animals, notably cats and dogs.

The cats would frequently keep an eye on something we couldn't see moving around the room, and they would hiss at nothing at other times.

As a result, my younger sister and I have been through several terrible situations.

In the middle of the night, something would frequently enter our room.

One time, I heard it slowly ascend the stairs, then a figure glanced around my door but immediately disappeared when it saw I was staring at it.

My sister reported that she had a recurring sensation of something settling at the foot of her bed. It was as if an adult was sitting there.

In addition, she occasionally caught a glimpse of the silhouette of an elderly gentleman.

Although she did not recall being scared by the presence, we sometimes pondered if it was our grandfather who had visited her.

I recall vividly waking up early when I was around 12 years old. I'm not sure where my sister had disappeared to, but I was the only one in the room.

Possibly 5:30 am, and the sun was just beginning to rise. My cat was howling, and I mean that most noisily.

Typical for my cat, he was calm and comfortable. But this time, he was freaking out, sprinting between my legs and the door, meowing his head off in terror. Then, finally, he simply raced out the front door and down the stairs.

I shook it off and rolled over when I woke up, hoping to fall back asleep.

However, I had a distinct impression that something wasn't quite right, so I returned my attention to the door to investigate.

A white female figure stood on the other side of the room, observing the proceedings.

I couldn't make out her face, but I could make out her long black straight hair and her body from where I was standing. Unfortunately, I could not see below her knees.

There was nothing else for it but to sit there and stare at this figure for what seemed an eternity.

Then, after a while, I could hear people moving around in the basement, and then the figure vanished.

We also used to have a German shepherd named Jilly, a great companion. We were on the verge of losing her because she was a ferocious guard dog, and if she heard or smelt anything strange, she would bark to be let out.

I was upstairs in my bedroom when I heard Jilly start barking. I went to investigate. I walked downstairs to let her out, expecting her to be waiting by the door, but she wasn't there. I was a little disappointed.

She was snarling and growling in the living room at nothing in particular.

I asked her if she wanted to go outside, but she ignored me and continued to bark at whatever she was looking at. So I gave up.

When she eventually came to a halt, she stared at me puzzled.

In the middle of the day, if I was ever alone at home, I would always hear voices from downstairs, which were almost always male voices. So I'd go down to see if somebody had stopped by, but I'd never see anyone and the voices would cease to be heard after that.

Once, I woke up from a sound slumber; I'm a pretty light sleeper, and rolled over so that I was looking toward the side of the room where my sister slept.

I noticed a small girl standing nearby, and it was most clearly not my sister. I could see my sister soundly asleep in her bed across the room for starters.

However, this young lady had thick, wild hair that reached down to her waist, and she was standing there with her arms hanging out to the side as if she were about to pounce on the opportunity.

I turned on the lights as quickly as I could, but I couldn't see anyone or anything that would have created such a prominent shadow.

My sister was in panic when I awoke the following day. All of her horse images had been pulled down from the walls.

In addition, several years after this particular occurrence, the folks who had previously owned our home came by to speak with my mother and express their gratitude. They inquired if anyone had seen the small girl who was said to haunt the residence.

The Hong Kong Hotel

―――

This happened five years ago, on November 24th and December 1st, 2005. Then, with my partner, I travelled to a vacation destination.

I've been taking vacations to Hong Kong since I was 13 years old. This, on the other hand, was an intriguing and memorable one.

I used to stay in a lovely high-rise hotel near the Mong Kok M.T.R. station, which was convenient for me.

Unfortunately, this hotel was in the process of being renovated at the time. As a result, we were transferred to a nearby hotel near Hong Kong Garden. I'd never done anything like this before.

When we first got to the hotel in the afternoon, we quickly packed our bags and ran into town to do some shopping. However, at 11 pm, we were both exhausted and decided to return to the hotel.

My girlfriend was so exhausted that she fell asleep on the double bed as soon as she stepped out of the shower. She slept facing the window, with the blanket covering her up to her head, whilst I slept facing the door.

Something terrible happened at 3 am. Just a few feet below my leg, someone was taking heavy breaths. And each time I see it, I get the impression that 'it' is getting closer and closer.

Suddenly, I have the impression that it is pretty close to me. I opened my eyes slightly to see what it was, but nothing was there.

But I was conscious of its presence, just beside me. And each breath "it" takes causes my heart rate to quicken...

I couldn't take it any longer because I was appalled and terrified. I push my blanket away and re-establish myself on my own two feet.

After that, I say (in Cantonese), "Please don't bother us; it's only a night, and we'll be out of here as soon as possible the next morning; please don't frighten my girlfriend. Please...."

Unaware, it came to a halt, and I began searching everywhere... Bathtub, shower, wardrobe, under the bed, and behind the curtain. Don't bother asking me why I dared. I honestly don't know where I found the guts to do it.

It does, however, only last for a brief time. It just lasted a few hours.

When we finished bathing the next day, my partner was getting ready in front of the mirror while I sat on the bed, putting on my shoe.

Furthermore, the breathing sounds came from directly behind her... and she was staring at me, helpless, as if she felt something was there...

"Pack your belongings and get out of here as quickly as possible," I said, motioning to her.

We told the Floor Manager of our dissatisfaction with the haunted room, and we were quickly shifted to a suite room. We were able to change to the new room with the help of the porter.

In the afternoon, we went to a park. I got her a small camera, which she used to shoot many photos.

This includes the large fish in the tank. It wasn't extremely packed because it was a weekday.

My girlfriend suggested we develop the images after that, but I suggested we wait until the end of the holiday.

We went back for supper after that, and everything seemed to be back on track after that first-day event... until.

We developed and gathered our images five days earlier, on a December morning in 2005. On the drive back to the hotel, I went through the photos to brush up on our languages when I handed them to her. She then noticed a "thing"... She observed that the spotlight was reflected in the water as she was photographing the enormous fishes in the tank, so she chose to photograph them. But there was one in particular... where a distinct and formed image replaced the 'Flash' reflection... "THE FACE OF AN OLD LADY."

I know all of those photos were taken when no one was around. So, where did the "face" come from?

Because it was so bright and clear, you could tell it was there, glaring at us. So I double-checked the negative and found it as well.

Before leaving the hotel, I showed it to the Floor Manager and informed him that she had been following us during our stay. Please make some improvements to the room... it's haunted!

I did not keep the snapshot, which I am unsure if he has kept.

After several failed attempts, I destroyed the negative when I got home, hoping to check with Fujifilm and Kodak about redeveloping the shot without the face. They all maintained, though, that they couldn't.

Unfortunately, this is not the end of the story. Our relationships took a sharp turn for the worst after the trip, which had never happened before. We may start a dispute at any minute. We cannot compromise and give in to one another anymore, no matter how little or big the issues are.

So we split up last year, and every time we patched back up, it lasted no longer than a week.

For some reason, I'll find methods to push her away and make her frustrated and angry with me. I'm not sure why I'm doing it. I just don't understand why. It simply comes and goes... It bothers me whenever she returns to me... something I am all too familiar with because my now ex-girlfriend is still around.

Zombies

―――

One night, I had a vivid nightmare about zombies that I still remember. They approached me and began yanking at my clothes.

I could still feel them pulling at me as I awakened. They were in my room, crawling over my bed and grabbing my clothes and hair.

I turned on my light and blinked furiously until they were no longer visible. Then, finally, I let out a sigh of relief and raised my head.

A black mass appeared nearby, a little more than four feet away. IT SLID INTO MY CLOSET LIKE A BULLET when I looked at it in the eyes.

I was alone at home on a cold, dark winter night a few years later, reading a book on the couch, when something happened.

Thunder, my sister's cat, was dozing on the arm of the recliner that she had climbed up onto.

After passing through the living room, a ghostly greyish apparition entered my parents' bedroom.

My cat Thunder had been watching it with me, and her eyes were fixed on the point where it had vanished, so I might have concluded it was a trick of the light.

My parents redecorated their bedroom when I was between 15 and 18. They uncovered a bible while pulling down the wall in their closet.

We assume it was written in German, and the strangest thing about it was that the margins appeared to be singed. We were, of course, aware that the house had been destroyed by fire many years previously.

My parents wanted to keep the Bible out of the house, but I insisted on substituting something else. They did listen, but the damage had already been done, in my opinion.

As a result, my sister and I didn't get much sleep until the house remodel was finished. As a result, we both had nightmares and woke up terrified every night.

We would occasionally hear noises in the middle of the night, such as whispers or footsteps. Following that, we began waking up with injuries that we couldn't pinpoint.

Our wrists were covered with finger-shaped bruises, I had a long burn running down the side of my face, and my sister had three terrible scratches on the back of her thorax.

After the structure was finished, things began to settle down for the most part, although we still heard footsteps when we were alone in the house, and I was frequently called by name when I was there.

I've since moved out of the house. My sister lives at home, but she refuses to talk about what happened there.

Peeping Tom

———

M ore than ten years ago, I was still living in Jurong West Blk 546, which was closer to my secondary school than my last address.

My regular nighttime routine included watching T.V. until 11 pm and conversing with my partner until 2 am. Following this incident, I never stayed up late at that house again.

During my school years, I live with a cousin and my grandma.

Except on weekends, only the three of us in the house because my parents prefer to stay at my grandmother's house during the week. After all, it's closer to their place of work.

On one occasion, my cousin went to a school camp and left my grandmother and me at home.

She usually goes to bed at 8 pm, and we turn off all of the lights in the corridor save the one in my room.

I was conversing with my partner in the middle of the night when someone or something opened my door, which was meant to be locked.

I spotted a black shadow peering into my room. I couldn't see it clearly because I wasn't wearing my glasses, but I could see its head swinging left and right as if hunting for something. After about 5 seconds, it has gone.

At first, I thought it was my grandmother. Still, after giving it some thought, it would be tough for her to sprint from my room to hers in less than 10 seconds, especially since she is over 75 years old.

I hung up the phone at 5:30 pm and wrapped myself in my blanket for the night.

Even after 15 years, it still frightens me. I've had multiple supernatural experiences during my army career, like sensing peculiar things in the field and hearing strange noises at night, but experiencing something paranormal makes me feel so uneasy that I practically pee my pants.

I'm glad I wasn't wearing my glasses because who knows what I might have seen on the shadow figure's face if I had.

I wonder if anyone else has had similar experiences with paranormal activity; I'd love to know what I witnessed.

Children Playing Marbles

————

Your mind is racing, and you're trying to sleep. You, on the other hand, are unable to sleep. It's that terrible clanging sound from above, I swear.

Someone from above appeared to be dumping marbles on the floor. You shake your head, thinking it's probably the children's fault; their parents must be insane for allowing their children to stay up so late.

When I strain my ears to hear it, I hear the faint sound of children's laughter.

They'll be asleep soon, and you'll be able to sleep as soundly as they do.

On the other hand, the noise does not stop, and I've had enough. Enraged, I stomped up the stairs to give my annoying upstairs neighbours a piece of my mind.

Although you ring their doorbell, I am ignored.

So I hammered on the door, yelling at them to exert some parental control over their children for my sanity. They, however, do not respond.

"Can you simply tell me what you're doing in there?" I yell.

The family's next-door neighbour, his face visibly irritated, walks out to greet them. He simply rolls his eyes when you complain about his next-door neighbour.

You might be hearing things because they left a month ago. "The house is empty," he says as he snaps his fingers and closes his window.

So, who's playing with marbles if the apartment is empty?

Later, I discovered that the Hong Kong Development Board inhabitants had complained about the sound of marbles or coins falling from the ceiling.

Even though the occurrence is usually linked to the pipe network, the ghosts of children have been postulated as a probable origin of the weird noises, especially when the flat above is abandoned or vacant.

According to some Singapore Ghost Hunters, the "marble dropping" sounds are more frequently heard in older units.

The Chinese Cemetery

———

There are many Chinese cemeteries in and around Petaling Jaya if you know where to look. Another one has a long road that goes through it; it is roughly 250m long and is placed at the back of the cemetery.

Chole and Linda, two of my friends, had to send a male friend home at 3 am, and they had to go through this graveyard twice to get there.

They dropped him off around 3 am and used that stretch of road to get onto the Federal Highway, which was a long drive.

"Do you smell, Chloe?" June exclaimed as soon as they arrived at the end of the road.

Chloe, who was driving at the time, quickly lifted her hand to raise the rear-view mirror to her eye level.

They were smelling a really strong floral perfume that was almost smothering them.

Chloe upped the level of the radio while driving, remained perfectly silent, and pressed the pedal. She drove, as usual, her gaze fixed on the road ahead.

Cindy pushed the mirror away from them because they were both aware that someone, or more precisely, something, was in the car with them at the time. She isn't interested in finding out what is behind her back.

As soon as they passed down the stretch of road, the aroma vanished almost as quickly as it had appeared.

Student Ghost

We sat through long days of classes and lectures, peering out the windows and wishing we were somewhere else. Then, when the bell rings, you rush from your seat and sprint past the sacred halls of learning to freedom.

However, there is a reason these halls are known as "sacred" – some pupils never return.

Every school has its own story to tell.

Our school's toilet cubicle is constantly locked, so you can't use it.

It hasn't been opened once, and it's challenging to have a look above or underneath it.

Because I've been wondering what's in there since my first day of school.

I've tried everything, but the lock won't budge, and every time I ask the cleaning auntie, she gives you a dismal look and drives you away with her broom, so you're stuck. So mop instead, depending on the day.

I'm the only one awake on the eve of school camp because the rest of the group has gone to sleep.

I'm not sure why, but I find myself lured to the toilet, despite the door being locked. I step into the cubicle as if it were a dream, and the door suddenly unlocks.

I step forward and reach out to push the door wide, but the door swings open, and the hinges groan in reaction to your movement.

I'll never forget the vision of a girl slumped over the toilet bowl, her throat slashed, her body surrounded by a pool of blood!

Years later, I discovered that student spirits and ghosts are the restless souls of students who died while attending school.

In either instance, these superhuman pupils have been robbed of their youth and now wander through the corridors, sobbing and appealing with the cosmos for their misfortune.

Because they are dressed in uniform, they have the appearance of creepy students.

I also discovered that practically every school, particularly those abandoned, has them.

It has been proven that the longer a school has been open, the more spirits haunt its corridors and classrooms. It's the first time I've informed anyone about what happened that morning.

Story Haunted Kitchen

———

I'm going to tell you about an incident in my prior residence. In truth, I had a lot of interactions in the flat over my ten-year stay.

The kitchen has always been the creepiest room in the house, and it will continue to be so.

The kitchen is designed in the shape of an inverted 'l,' with the sink adjacent to the refrigerator, resulting in a restricted quantity of natural light flowing in through the window.

In any event, I'm typing on my computer in the living room, with my back to a big praying altar.

My mum used to work for and be an active member of a group. So that's how we ended up living on these premises. It was spacious, and we had more family members staying there simultaneously.

However, my uncle, who used to live with us, recently moved out and took my late grandfather's tablet with him, so we've been hearing a lot of strange noises coming from the kitchen since he went.

Not to mention the talisman affixed to the outside wall of our house.

After that, it began to break apart over the front entryway. And I frequently remind my mother that the 'idol' of worship appears to be empty, as opposed to how it seemed in our old home in Bukit Merah.

After my school examinations, I would frequently stay up late to search the internet, communicate with friends, and play computer games till the early hours of the morning.

Furthermore, I will always feel that someone is constantly watching me from somewhere in the kitchen every night.

Every time I turn around, nothing is there. But, aside from the glances, there will always be this 'thud' sound, which sounds like someone laying a cup down, coming from the kitchen, which was where it used to be. This was the location of my grandfather's tablet.

I assumed it was my father since he would occasionally wake up in the middle of the night and walk to the kitchen for a cup of water without turning on the house lights.

On the other hand, whenever I check on my father, he is usually fast asleep.

When I was happily gaming with my parents asleep, a huge bang occurred from the interior of our shoe cabinet, which I considered the worst thing that could have happened to me. I felt a tremendous amount of pressure behind my neck. It seemed as if someone had rushed up behind me and stood there.

I couldn't turn around because I was too afraid, so I stood there for about a minute till the feeling subsided slightly. There was no one around when I peered around.

Our shoe cabinet has been installed in the house. So it can't be any kind of mouse sneaking in without being noticed!

That was the evening's final straw. As a result, I swiftly shut down my computer and retired to my bed.

Haunted Blanket

———

This took place in the year 1993. I was living in a Bishan apartment complex at the time.

It was a rainy, stormy night, and it was one of those nights when I couldn't get asleep and couldn't sleep.

So I went to the kitchen and poured myself a cup of Milo before sitting on the living room sofa and watching T.V. I had planned to watch several videotapes on my computer.

He was in primary school at the time, and he tended wrapping himself in his huge blanket from head to toe and waking me up in the middle of the night to help him to the restroom. At the time, I was in high school.

He walked through the living room and towards the kitchen, stopping near the kitchen to use the restroom.

On that particular night, he exited his room, which he had completely covered with a blanket, and proceeded through the living room, where I was, to the kitchen toilet.

He didn't ask me to follow him since I was already awake and sitting on the sofa in the living room, watching television, so he didn't feel as frightened as I imagined.

It was amusing that he didn't turn on the kitchen and toilet lights, as he had done on previous evenings, which I thought was odd.

In any case, I'd rather ignore him. So before heading to my room, I decided to turn off the video recorder and the television till I was exhausted. But, unfortunately, my younger brother had not yet returned from the bathroom, startled me.

It's also possible that he went back to his room and I didn't notice. As a result, when I walked into his room, I noticed that his bed was vacant.

The entire home was pitch black because I had turned off all of the lights by this point. I then went into the kitchen, anticipating him to yell at me for "leaving him in the dark." But, instead, he remained deafeningly silent.

When I turned on the kitchen light, I spotted my younger brother standing outside the toilet, still covered in a blanket. So, of course, I dialled 911 right away.

"Are you finished?" "Let's get some rest, shall we?" "I told him," I said. He, on the other hand, stood there doing nothing.

"Could you just explain to me what's going on?" Then, as I approached him and pulled away the blanket to better look at his face, I got the shock of my life!

Because there was nothing behind the blanket, which I misunderstood for my brother's body!

The blanket was utterly devoid of anything beneath it! So there are only empty seats!

As a result, I attempted to remain calm and turn around to return to my bedroom. However, all I did was leave the blanket on the kitchen floor.

The distance between me and my room appeared to be quite considerable, as I was aware of someone or something standing behind me, still staring at me.

When I got to my room, I quickly shut and locked the door before retiring to my bed for the night. I'm not even going to look out the window.

The next day, I asked my younger brother if he had used the restroom the night before. Again, he refused to say anything or accept what had happened.

Room For A Student

———

This happened shortly after I finished my studies in the north. When I arrived, it was well beyond midnight.

In Alor Setar, I was alone. I had planned to return to Kuala Lumpur later that evening.

However, I was stranded in the nation since my parents could not deposit the needed monies.

Furthermore, there was no online banking at the time. As a result, funds had to be deposited using a machine.

I only had RM5 left in my wallet to continue my story, and my car's fuel was running low.

We couldn't sleep in the car because we were terrified something terrible would happen. After all, Alor Setar is like a ghost town after midnight.

WHEN I sought for a surau or a masjid, I FOUND IT DARK AND SHUTTERED.

I couldn't call any of my close friends because cell phones were considered a luxury at the time. Unfortunately, due to financial constraints, students are unable to afford one.

As a result, I looked for a two-star motel out of desperation. I've found one. I prefer two-star motels since the proprietor usually controls the front desk.

So I walked in and explained my predicament to the receptionist. As previously stated, I need a place to stay tonight but lack the means to pay the required deposit.

However, I promised them that I would pay the next day after my parents had transferred the monies.

She was initially hesitant, so I handed her my student I.D. card and ordered her to keep my credentials as collateral if she agreed to let me remain with her.

I assume the receptionist went into the house to speak with her husband. Later, she returned and agreed, but she insisted on an additional RM50 for the room. Because I was desperate, I had no choice but to agree.

She handed me the keys to a first-floor room, which I instantly entered. But, unfortunately, there was only one room, and there were no other rooms nearby.

When I walked in, I was surprised by how much space there was. "How thoughtful of her to furnish me with this room," I thought.

I had planned to provide a simple room with simply one small bed and no television or bathroom.

On the other hand, this room was incredibly roomy, with a queen-size bed and a large bathroom.

So, I didn't bother changing my clothing; instead, I jumped onto the bed and wanted to sleep.

This is the point at which the terror begins. I awoke at roughly 3 am. The water was rushing through the pipe, and I could hear it. I simply walked into the toilet and turned off the water since I was exhausted.

Then I got out of bed and returned to my room. Following that, I could hear quiet whispering.

I maintained my cool. I just want to sleep. Then I got the unmistakable sensation that someone had simply positioned themselves directly behind me.

OK, I'm becoming a little nervous now. So I simply wrapped the blanket around my entire body from head to toe and hoped for the best.

Then I heard chains being dragged across the floor of my bedroom. Following that, I heard a woman's voice that sounded like she was crying and felt the blanket tug slightly.

I badly wanted to leave the room, but I was too terrified to lift the blanket and find out what was bothering me.

Please bear with me as a result. Then, I closed my eyes and recited whatever Bible verses came to me.

As it turned out, the disturbance lasted all night, and by the time I realised it, it was 6 am. Then everything went back to normal.

I awoke at 6 am, went to the front desk, and asked to use the phone to call my folks. OK, said reception. They informed me that the funds had already been sent to the bank.

To make a long story short, I paid the fee and checked out as soon as I was through. I was so terrified that I didn't even bother showering that morning.

I pulled off at one of the rest sites along the way to shower and sleep in the car before continuing my journey back to Kuala Lumpur.

This was something I never told anyone. I don't want to raise a commotion later on by phoning the hotel and complaining about being given a bad room, including my parents.

My friends are also unaware of what is going on.

After keeping this narrative to myself for over a decade, I now regard it as a personal adventure that I will never share with anyone else.

So, what was that dragging sound, and who was the crying woman in that motel room?

Demons In My Sleep

I was studying for examinations at the time, so my sleeping patterns were erratic. I awoke abruptly one night at 3 am.

I couldn't move anything, not even my eyes, even though my skin touched the blanket.

As time passed, my breathing grew laboured and harsh. It was quite unsettling to be unable to move or see.

I was startled awake by the impression of "someone" sitting on the edge of my bed, and weight was approaching me. It moved slowly towards me from left to right, as if its hands and feet were crawling towards me. Then, I swear I heard a creaking bed in the distance.

That beast was soon sitting on my chest, making it impossible for me to breathe.

My ears were ringing, and I couldn't open my eyes despite my best attempts.

I was astounded to see shadowy figures circling me and running around the room when I did.

I couldn't comprehend what they were saying since they whispered something nonsensical.

I said my prayers to myself in my head. I was eventually able to squirm free of my paralysis and walk after about a minute of earnest praying.

When I went into my parents' room to tell them about it, they said, "Go to bed."

Haunted Hospital

———

I was a second-year nursing student at College East in 2004, and I am still there today. I was assigned to S.G.H. for my I.A. because passing a module in my course was required.

While I was linked to the ward, there was an incident in block 2, level 4. Those in the nursing profession should understand what I'm talking about.

On my fourth week, I was assigned to that ward and will stay there for two months.

As a nurse, I served a patient whose kidney was in the second stage of renal failure, indicating that he was not far from the third stage of renal failure, which would cause him to die.

I assisted him for a week and learned more about his family and personal life. He was a lovely uncle who used to make me laugh to help me get through my shifts at work faster.

As a result, I spend slightly more time speaking with him than with the other patients. One of the benefits of being a student nurse is working on your schedule.

After a solid three weeks of serving him, he has become a family buddy.

Then, as my shift ended on a Friday afternoon, I bid goodbye to him and pledged to see him, a better version of myself the following Monday. Unfortunately, however, that was the last time I saw him.

When Monday rolled along, I went to work as usual. However, I was alone at the counter in the early morning hours, waiting for my shift to begin.

As he passed past the counter to the bathroom, I recognised my favourite uncle. "Aye, uncle!" I exclaimed to him. He replied. So you're already able to walk?

That's fantastic, that's fantastic. Is it OK if you take a stroll?

Do you want me to help you, or do you want me to assist you?

"It's all right, boy," he said gently. I'm fine, I'm fine, I'm fine. You have already been an enormous help.

You have a task to complete, don't you? Go, go, go...then he keeps walking as he turns the corner and enters the men's lavatory. "Lad," he grumbled as he turned around. "I sincerely appreciate everything."

As a nurse, you will be exposed to a variety of circumstances. So I went about my daily routine. However, as the shift changed and reports were sent around, the tone changed.

It was sad that my uncle's report was not mentioned in the daily report. As a result, I begin to mistrust the position of my favourite uncle.

The nurses on staff were all mystified as to why you enquired about him. I then remarked that I had just observed him walk to the restroom.

The entire team was taken aback! Then a senior staff member approached me and urged me to stop talking.

Then she told me that he had died the day before from rapidly increasing renal failure, which the doctors could not reverse.

I was initially sceptical, so I went to his old bed to double-check. I then went to the bathroom to see if any of his possessions were still there, but they weren't.

There was no one inside! What I was hearing was unbelievable. After a while, I accepted his death and read his case notes.

He was confirmed dead at 6.30 am, when I had last seen him on that specific day.

About The Author

———

G ranger T Barr currently resides in London with his wife and dog. He has researched paranormal activities and true-life stories both locally and beyond.

Thank again for reading this book,

please give us the thumbs-up.

GET A FREE GHOST E-BOOK BY SUBSCRIBING TO OUR MAILING LIST[1]:

Get more freebies, goodies and instant new book release announcements!

https://digitaldome.sendibble.com/True-Ghost-Stories-Perma-Free-Ghost-E-book

---

1. *https://digitaldome.sendibble.com/True-Ghost-Stories-Perma-Free-Ghost-E-book*

Other Books by This Author

———

You may be interested in other books within the *Ghostly Encounters Series*:

True Ghost Stories and Hauntings: Real-Life Personal Short Ghost Stories In And Around Britain

13 short ghost stories.

Real Ghost Stories and Hauntings: True-Life Short Ghost Stories (*Ghostly Paranormal Encounters*)

19 short ghost stories.

True Ghost Stories & Hauntings Chilling Tales For Adults: Real Life Paranormal Ghostly Supernatural Encounters Collection From Around The World, and More.

GET A FREE GHOST E-BOOK BY SUBSCRIBING TO OUR MAILING LIST[1]:

Get more freebies, goodies and instant new book release announcements!

https://digitaldome.sendibble.com/True-Ghost-Stories-Perma-Free-Ghost-E-book

Bible Verses for Protection

1 Peter 5:8

King James Version

Be sober, be vigilant; because your adversary the devil, as a roaring lion, walketh about, seeking whom he may devour.

John 3:16

King James Version

For God so loved the world, that he gave his only begotten son, that whosoever believeth in him should not perish, but have everlasting life.

Ephesians 6:11

King James Version

Put on the whole armour of God, that ye may be able to stand against the wiles of the devil.

Psalm 23:4

King James Version

Yea, though I walk through the valley of the shadow of death, I will fear no evil: for thou art with me; thy rod and thy staff they comfort me.

Psalm 121:7

King James Version

The Lord shall preserve thee from all evil: he shall preserve thy soul.

Psalm 62:2

King James Version

He only is my rock and my salvation; he is my defense; I shall not be greatly moved.

2 Timothy 1:7

King James Version

For God hath not given us the spirit of fear, but of power, and of love, and of a sound mind.

A.B.C.'s Of Salvation

———

J esus Christ is the only one who can save and protect your soul from the devil.

We are not promised our next breath.

Time is short. Please seek Jesus today!

The Gospel = Good News

New Testament Corinthians 15:1-4

ABC OF SALVATION

A - ADMIT

Admit you are a sinner and have made mistakes.

Romans 3:23

B - BELIEVE

Believe that Jesus is God's Son, died on the cross for you, and rose from the grave on the third day.

Romans 10:9-10

C - CONFESS

Confess with your mouth that Jesus is Lord of your life. Then, commit yourself to a life of following Jesus and serving others.

Romans 10:13

You WILL be saved.

Ghosts do not exist but demons do.

Don't miss out!

Visit the website below and you can sign up to receive emails whenever Granger T Barr publishes a new book. There's no charge and no obligation.

https://books2read.com/r/B-A-MMUL-PSCXB

BOOKS 2 READ

Connecting independent readers to independent writers.

Also by Granger T Barr

Ghostly Encounters
True Ghost Stories and Hauntings
Real Ghost Stories and Hauntings
Ghost Stories Collection
True Ghost Stories And Hauntings: Chilling Tales For Adults: Real Life Paranormal Ghostly Supernatural Encounters Collection From Around The World
Real Ghosts, True-Life Stories, And Hauntings: Paranormal Ghostly Supernatural Encounters
Haunted Hospitals: True Real Hospital Ghost Stories & Hauntings 25 Unexplained Supernatural Mysteries Of The Paranormal In Britain And America
What You Should Know About Ghosts, Objects And Places: Supernatural Guide To Paranormal Happenings And Investigations
Real Ghost Stories In The UK: True Haunted History Around Great Britain
Ghost Stories: 25 Supernatural Tales By Real People Based On True Events In And Around The Far East

Ingram Content Group UK Ltd.
Milton Keynes UK
UKHW010736280323
419292UK00001B/47

9 798201 648480